This annual belongs to

_____

First published by Parragon in 2009

Parragon
Queen Street House
4 Queen Street
Bath BA1 1HE, UK

www.chuggington.com

© Ludorum plc 2009

ISBN 978-1-84535-409-1

Printed in China

ANNUAL 2010

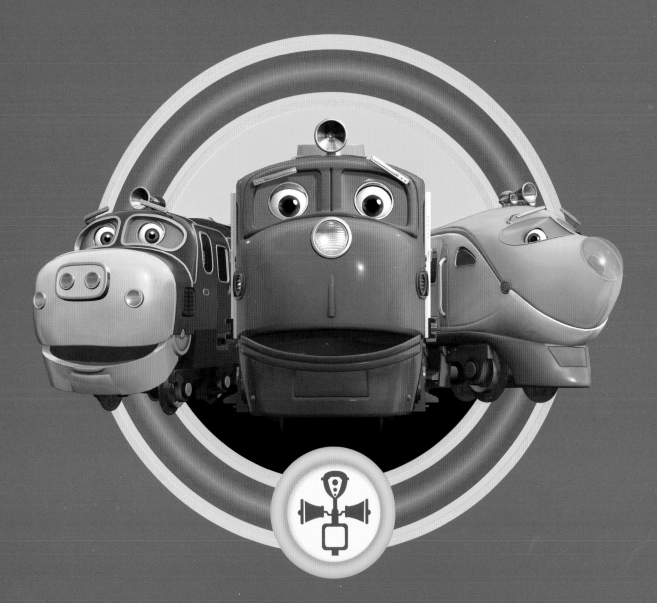

Parragon

Bath · New York · Singapore · Hong Kong · Cologne · Delhi · Melbourne

CONTENTS

Who can you see?	8
Wordsearch	9
Koko's trail	10
Wilson	11
Koko	12
Dot to dot	13
CLUNKY WILSON - STORY	14
Shadow shapes	20
Brewster	21
Emery	22
Can you find?	23
Matching pair	24
Colouring fun	25
Spot the difference	26
Missing pieces	28
Guess who?	29
Traintastic!	30
Dunbar	31
Old Puffer Pete	32
How many?	33
BRAKING BREWSTER - STORY	34
What time is it?	40
Big and small	42
Harrison	43
Chatsworth	44
Guess who?	45
Colour match	46
Colouring fun	47
Copy and colour	48
How many red trains?	50
Dot to dot	51
Odd ones out	52
Wilson's maze	53
CAN'T CATCH KOKO - STORY	54
Odd ones out	60
Action Chugger	61
Mtambo	62
Guess who?	63

WAKE UP CHUGGERS!

What's the sound?	64
Colouring fun	65
Copy and colour	66
Shape finder	68
Spot the difference	70
Calley	72
Koko's maze	73
WAKE UP WILSON – STORY	**74**
Copy and colour	80
Counting fun	82
Matching pairs	83
Which tunnel?	84
Dot to dot	85
Colour the scene	86
Wordsearch	87
Irving	88
What goes where?	89
Can you find?	90
Answers	92

WHO CAN YOU SEE?

Chuggington is home to lots of chuggers.
How many can you spot in this picture?
What are their names?

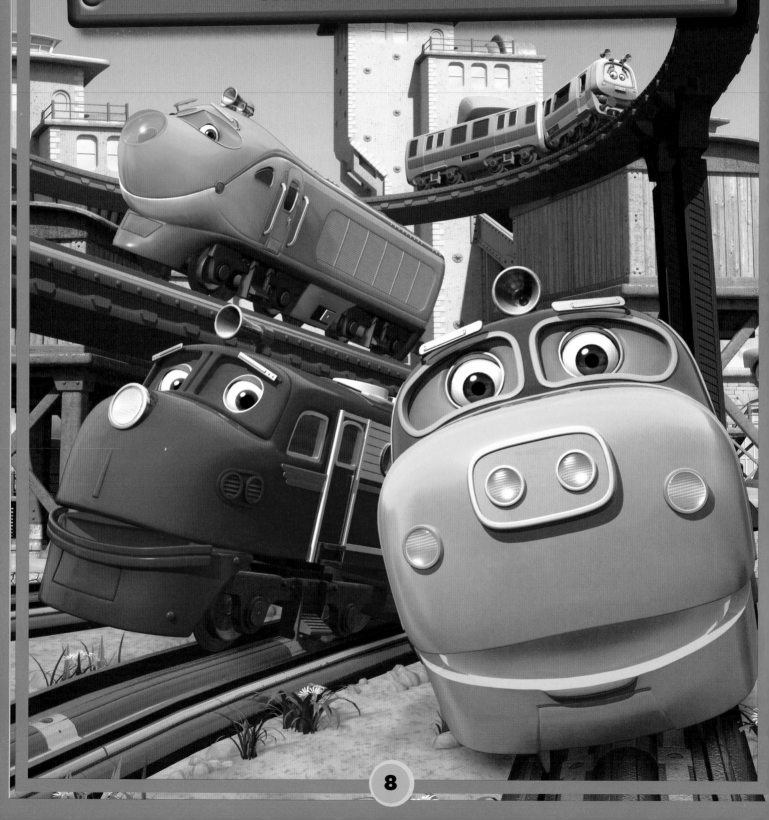

8

WORDSEARCH

Can you find the words listed below hidden in the grid? Circle each one you find.

KOKO

DUNBAR

WILSON

EMERY

B	T	I	O	M	E
E	M	E	R	Y	A
C	R	D	B	K	J
W	I	L	S	O	N
E	K	W	I	K	K
W	J	A	C	O	Y
D	U	N	B	A	R

KOKO'S TRAIL

Vee needs Koko and Wilson to go to the farm.
Help Koko find her way to Wilson.

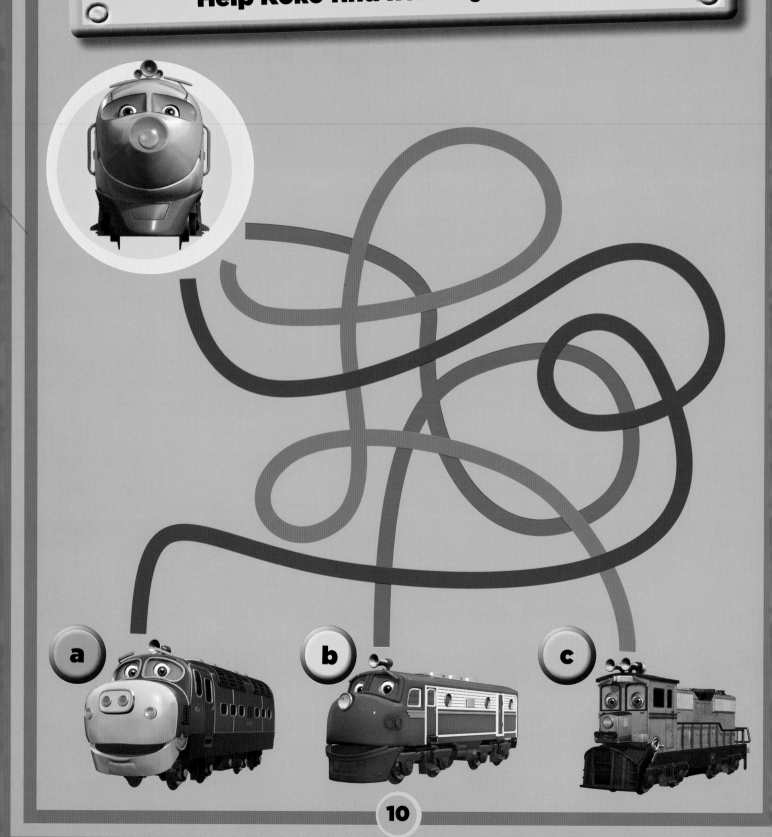

a

b

c

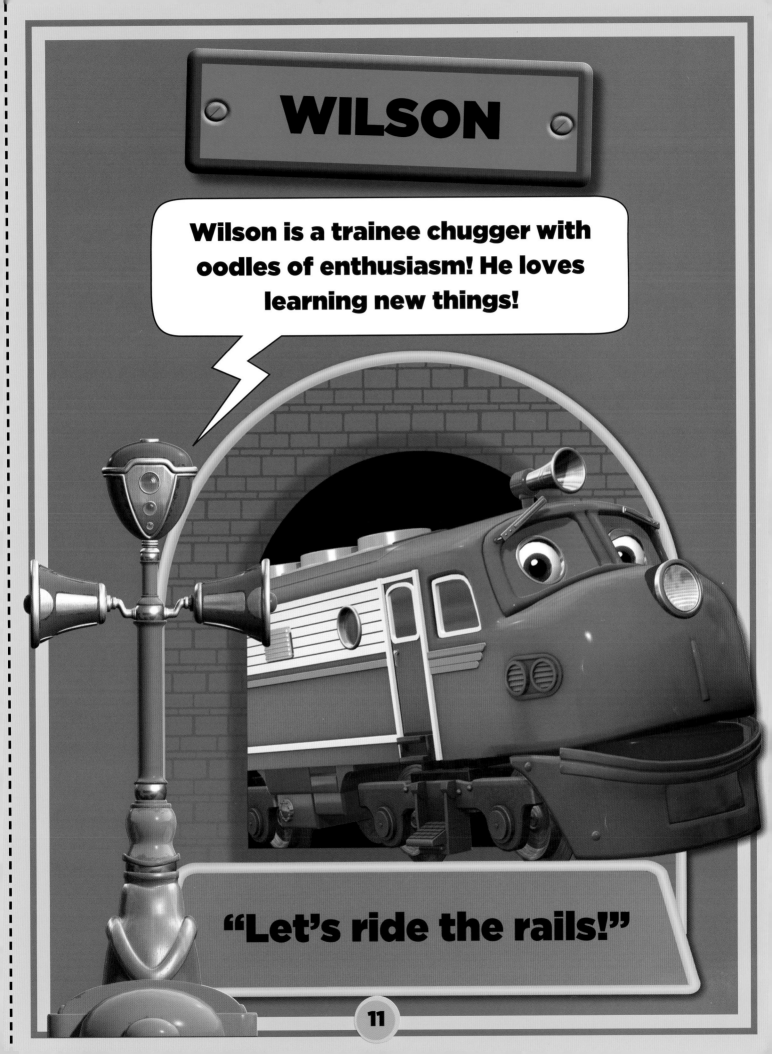

KOKO

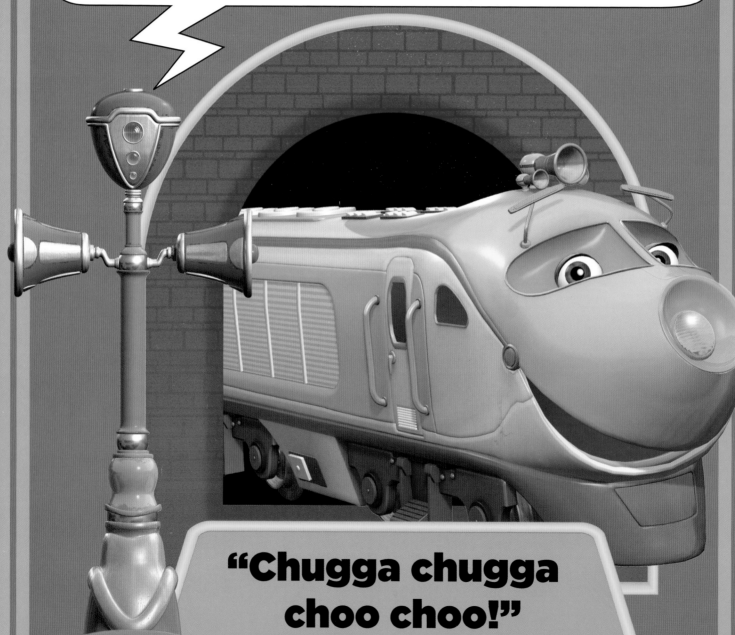

Koko is a trainee electric chugger who loves to go fast! She loves to explore the world around her and have fun adventures! What's your favourite Koko adventure?

"Chugga chugga choo choo!"

DOT TO DOT

Join the dots to finish this absotootly great picture of Calley, then colour it in.

CLUNKY WILSON

1 One day, Wilson, Koko and Brewster were about to have a race. Suddenly, they heard loud noises from the repair shed. Wilson felt very scared and didn't want to find out what the noises were.

BANG! CRASH!

BEEP! BEEP!

2 Emery joined the others and told them about the repair shed. **"Puffer Pete was in there for a whole week once. They took all his wheels off!"** Wilson gasped – he never wanted to go near the repair shed.

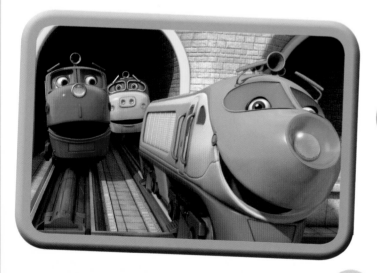

3 The chuggers said goodbye to Emery and set off. **"Last one to the bumpers has square wheels!"** called Koko.

4 Koko zoomed off ahead but Wilson really wanted to catch up and win the race. Poor Brewster began to puff – he couldn't keep up with the others!

ZOOOM!

5 Koko slowed down as she reached the bumpers at the end of the track. But Wilson didn't see them in time!

CRASH!

As he tried to back up, his wheels made a loud clunking noise. Something was wrong!

6 Vee called the three trainees to the loading yard. **"Wahay! It's training time!"** said Wilson, excitedly. But his wheels began to make a scraping sound as he entered the depot.

SCRAPE! CLUNK!

7 Emery could see Wilson from the track above. **"I think your wheel has dropped off,"** Emery teased. He was only joking but Wilson was worried – he didn't want to go to the repair shed.

8 In the loading yard, Wilson buckled up to a boxcar. His wheels were still making funny noises.

CLUNKETY! CLUNK!

9 Wilson pretended to cough to hide the noise of his wheels. He knew Dunbar would send him to the repair shed if something was wrong.

10 Vee sent the chuggers to take some things from the farm to the fair. Koko's boxcar was loaded with eggs, Brewster's with vegetables and Wilson took the cream.

11 Felix the farmer asked Wilson if he could have a ride to the fair too. He was hoping his cream would win a prize.

12 But the journey was so bumpy... poor Felix spilled juice all over himself!

13 It was no good! Wilson would have to go to the repair shed! The red chugger shakily followed his friends back to the depot.

14 In the repair shed, Morgan the mechanic looked underneath Wilson. **"You're really brave,"** Morgan told him. "Most chuggers are nervous the first time they have to get fixed."

15 This made Wilson feel much better. Morgan fixed his broken suspension spring and Wilson was as good as new!

16 Later that day, Vee called Wilson back to the fair to collect Felix. The bumpy ride had shaken up the cream so much that it became really thick! Wilson felt terrible.

17 But the farmer told him he won first place for producing the most delicious butter! Wilson was full of pride as the farmer placed the rosette on him.

18 Wilson had learned his lesson though. **"Next time there's something wrong with me, I'm going straight to the repair shed!"**

SHADOW SHAPES

Can you match the chuggers to their shadows?
Draw a line to each correct shadow.

1

2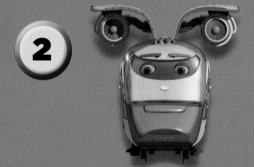

3

4

A

B

C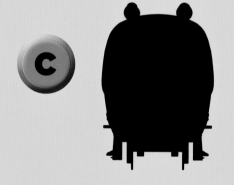

D

BREWSTER

Brewster is strong and can carry really heavy loads. Everyone in Chuggington knows they can count on Brewster!

"Honking horns!"

EMERY

Emery is a transport train who carries people around Chuggington. He likes whizzing up and down the tracks and teasing his chugger friends.

"Made you look, made you steer, made you have to change a gear!"

CAN YOU FIND?

Can you spot these items in the scene below?
Circle the ones you find.

MATCHING PAIR

Only two of these pictures of Chuggington superhero Action Chugger match exactly. Can you spot them?

1

2

3

4

COLOURING FUN

Zephie is a young scissor-lift trolley. She is bright green and often gets very excited.

SPOT THE DIFFERENCE

Can you find five differences between the two pictures of Mtambo below? Circle the ones you find.

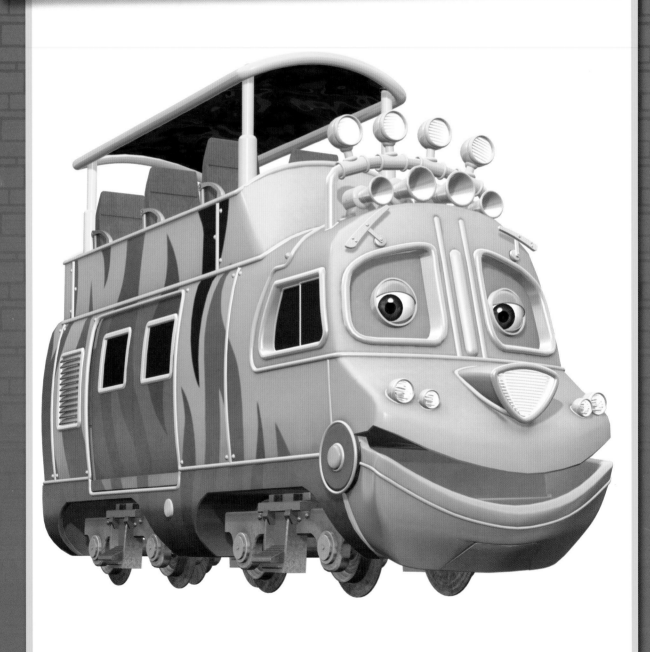

26

Mtambo has travelled all over the world and the trainee chuggers love to hear his tales of adventure!

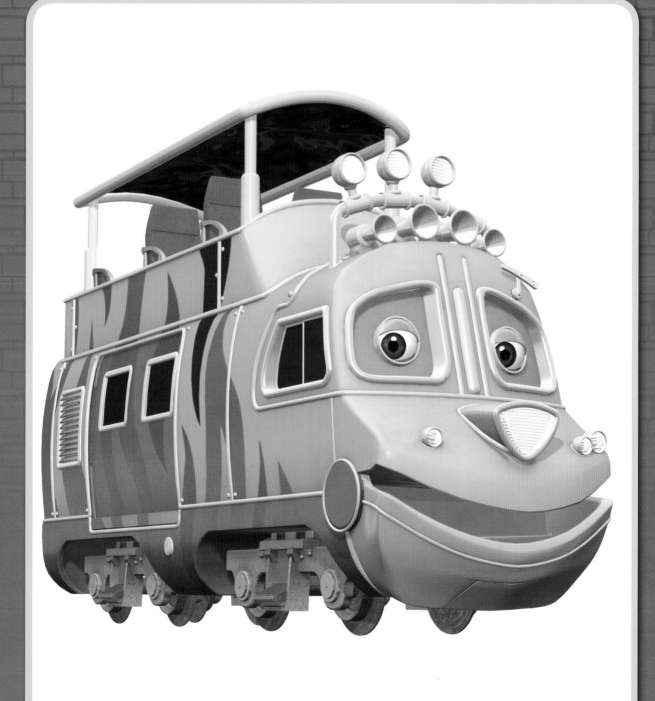

MISSING PIECES
Which jigsaw pieces complete this picture?
Circle the one that doesn't fit.

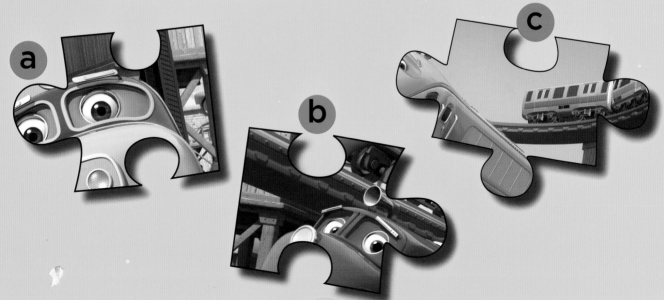

a

b

c

GUESS WHO?

Match the chuggers to their colours and favourite sayings by drawing a line between them.

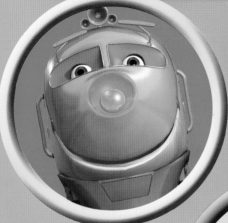

- red chugger
- "Let's ride the rails!"

- white chugger
- "Made you look, made you steer!"

- green chugger
- "Traintastic!"

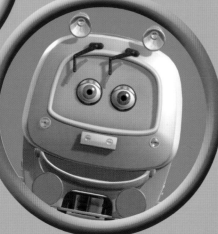

- blue and yellow chugger
- "Honking horns!"

TRAINTASTIC!

There are lots of exciting new words to learn in Chuggington. Some of them are also noisy words so join in with the sounds.

horn

I can beep my horn to let other chuggers know I'm coming.

HONK! HONK!

I carry people from one place to another in my carriages.

carriage

At night, I switch my headlight on to see where I'm going.

headlight

funnel

PUFF! PUFF!

I'm a steam engine, so steam puffs out of my funnel.

DUNBAR

Dunbar teaches the trainees everything they need to know about how to be good chuggers.

"Let's get those wheels to the rails!"

OLD PUFFER PETE

Old Puffer Pete is the oldest train in Chuggington. He is 150 years old! He is a steam engine and slowly puffs up and down the tracks.

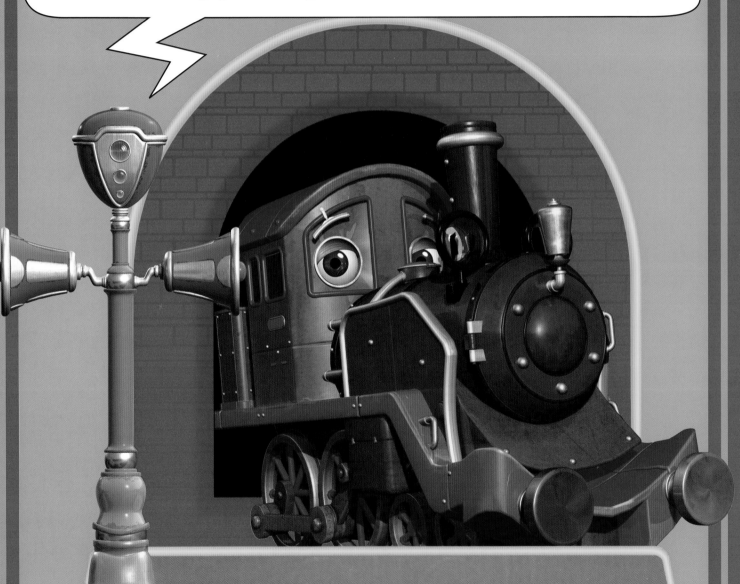

"Chuff, chuff, chuff!"

HOW MANY?

How many green trains can you see in the boxes below?

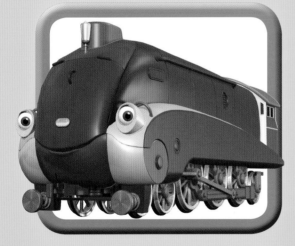

BRAKING BREWSTER

1 One morning, Vee had an exciting job for Brewster and Wilson. **"It's training time!"** said Wilson, excitedly. But Brewster wanted to be back in time to practice his new moves.

2 In the loading yard, Dunbar gave Brewster and Wilson hopper cars for training. He showed them what to do when they had a heavy load. **"Doors...drop...load. Got it,"** said Brewster, confidently.

3 Wilson found it really hard at first – but he kept trying. Then he did it!

"Wahay!"

4 The two chuggers started on their journey. Dunbar warned them that it was harder going downhill with a heavy load, so they must come back slowly. Wilson listened carefully, but Brewster had already whizzed ahead.

WHIZZZZZ!

5 Vee told the chuggers to go to the mountain quarry to collect stone. They were to take the left tunnel at the mountain.

"Let's ride the rails!"

6 On the platform next to them, Morgan the mechanic suddenly slipped over on some oil. Wilson watched as Morgan sprinkled sand over the oil so his feet could grip.

ZOOMMMM!

7 When Brewster and Wilson came out of the tunnel and looked up at the mountain, they saw it was a very long way away.

CHUG, CHUG, CHUG...

8 They climbed the track, higher and higher up the mountain. Suddenly there were two tunnels in front of them.

9 Wilson was unsure what tunnel they had to take. He wished he'd listened more carefully to Vee, but they went through the tunnel on the right.

10 Before long, the tracks began to slope downwards. **"Honking horns – we're going downhill!"** said Brewster, worriedly. They were going the wrong way! After turning around, they rushed back uphill and chose the tunnel on the left this time.

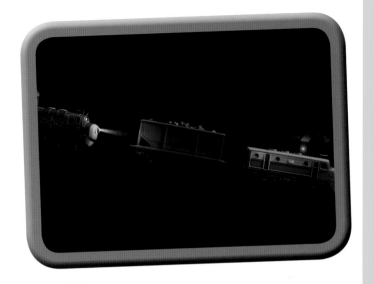

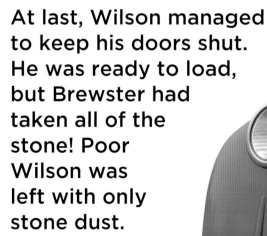

11 Finally, they reached the quarry. Karen, the quarry worker, loaded stones into Wilson's hopper car but Wilson struggled to keep his doors shut. Brewster was eager to finish the job quickly, so he offered to go first.

12 At last, Wilson managed to keep his doors shut. He was ready to load, but Brewster had taken all of the stone! Poor Wilson was left with only stone dust.

13 Brewster zoomed ahead, but Wilson remembered Dunbar's warning – to be extra careful going downhill. **"Downhill's easy peasy,"** Brewster said.

14 Suddenly, the track became very steep and Brewster sped down the mountainside, out of control! **"My brakes don't work. Help! I can't grip the rails!"** he cried.

AAAAAAAHHH!

15 As Wilson caught up with Brewster, he had an idea. He whizzed ahead of Brewster and dropped his load of stone dust on the track. **"Brake on the dust!"** Wilson called.

16 It worked! They both slowed down and came to a stop. **"Thanks, Wilson, you saved me,"** said Brewster, very relieved. Wilson had remembered that Morgan used the sand to help grip when he slipped on the oil.

17 The two chuggers made their way back to the depot. Vee was happy to see them.

"Good work, trainees. And there's still plenty of time left for you to practice, Brewster."

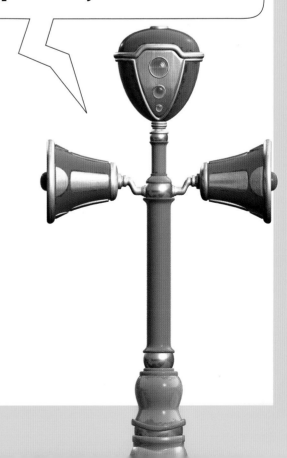

18 But Brewster had tried out enough new moves for one day. **"Now I know...if you're going downhill, you have to go..."** Brewster said, pausing. **"SLOW! HA HA!"** giggled Wilson and Brewster.

WHAT TIME IS IT?

Chuggington is very busy, the trains are always on the move! Read the time on the clocks to help these chuggers get to their jobs on time.

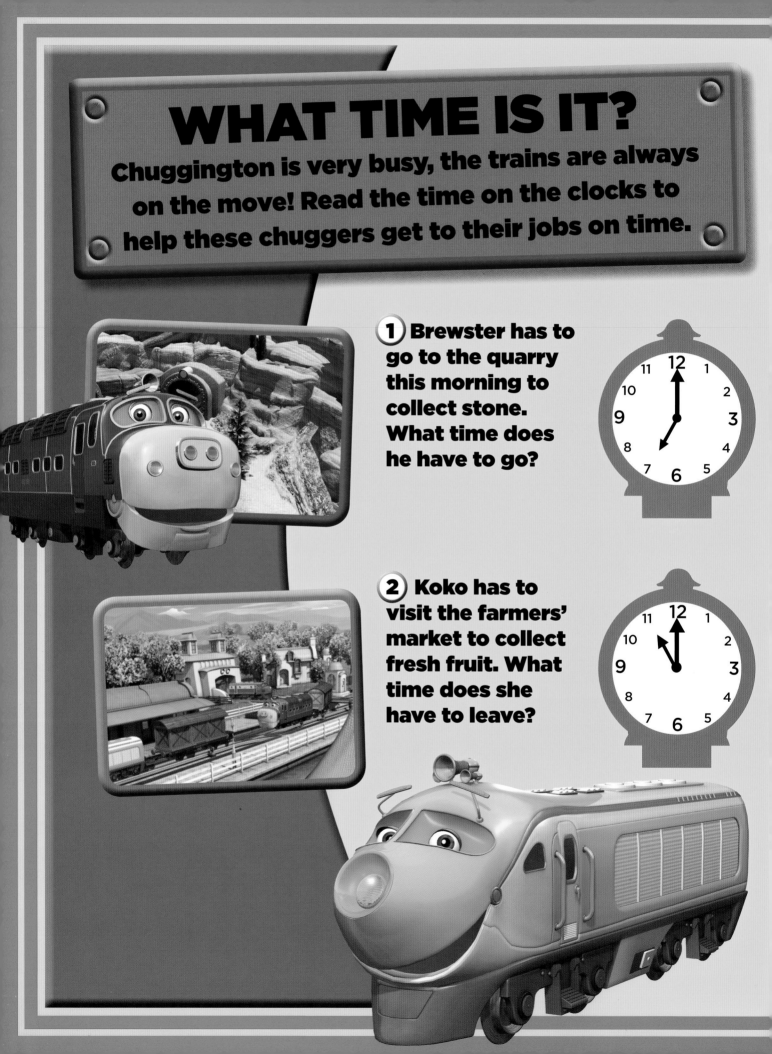

1 Brewster has to go to the quarry this morning to collect stone. What time does he have to go?

2 Koko has to visit the farmers' market to collect fresh fruit. What time does she have to leave?

3 The three trainees have a lesson with Dunbar at the rolling stock yard this afternoon. What time is the lesson?

4 Wilson needs to meet Morgan at the repair shed. What time does he have to be there?

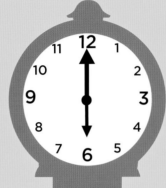

5 Harrison is giving Felix the Farmer a ride to the farmers' fair. What time does he need to meet Felix?

6 Frostini travels around Chuggington all day delivering his ice-cream. What time does he finish?

BIG AND SMALL

Look at the train pictures below. Who is the biggest chugger? Who is the smallest?

Harrison

Hodge

Zephie

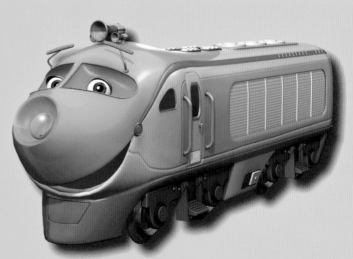

Koko

HARRISON

Harrison is well known as the fastest train in Chuggington. He always does the mail run, except when Koko, Brewster and Wilson had to help out.

The Great Chugger Champion

CHATSWORTH

Chatsworth is honest, polite and considerate. He lives in the upper level of the roundhouse with Harrison.

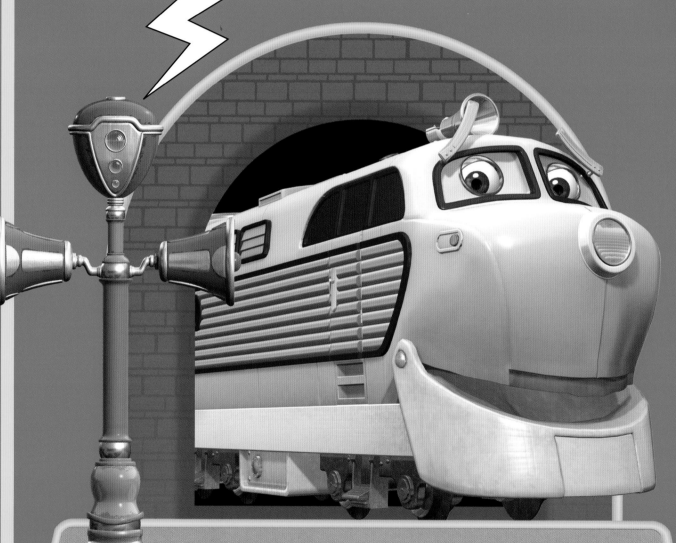

"Always put your best wheel forward!"

GUESS WHO?

This picture has got all mixed up. Can you unscramble it to find out who it is?

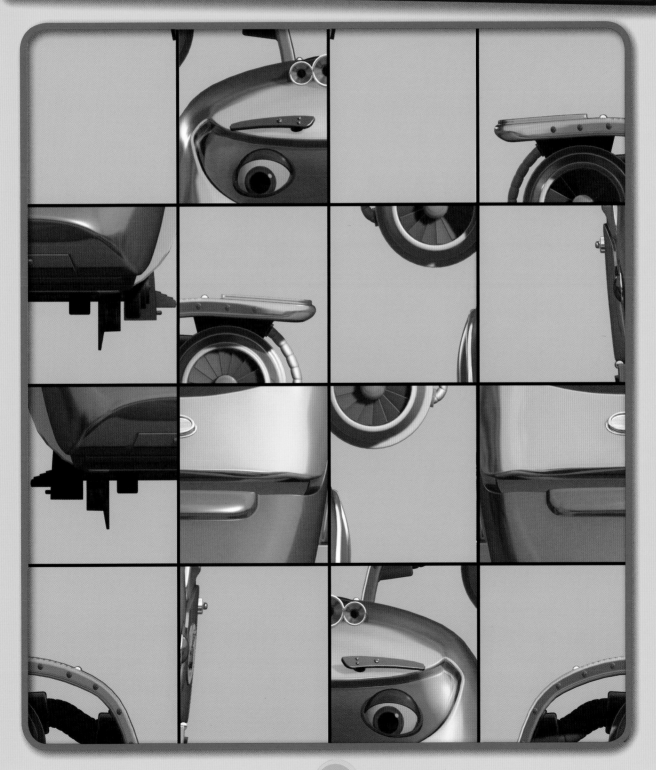

COLOUR MATCH
Can you match each chugger to their colour?
Draw a line between them.

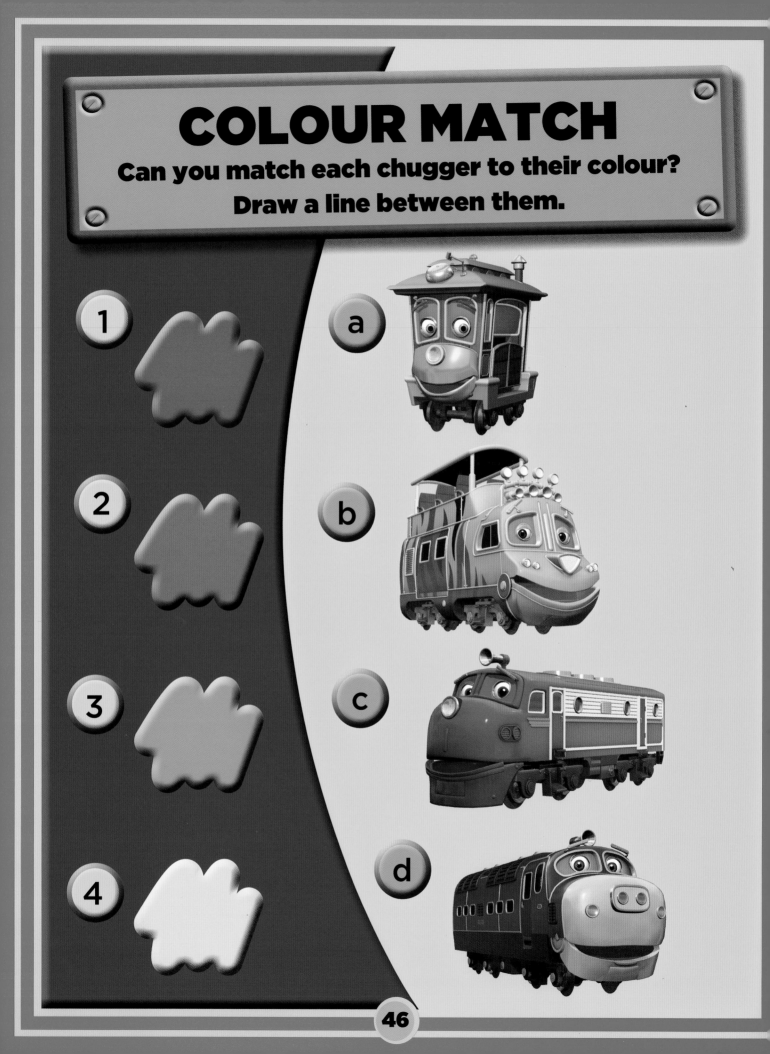

1

2

3

4

a

b

c

d

COLOURING FUN

**Brewster's paint is blue and yellow.
Which other chuggers are blue?**

COPY AND COLOUR

Copy the picture of Wilson into the grid on the next page, using the lines as a guide. Then colour your drawing.

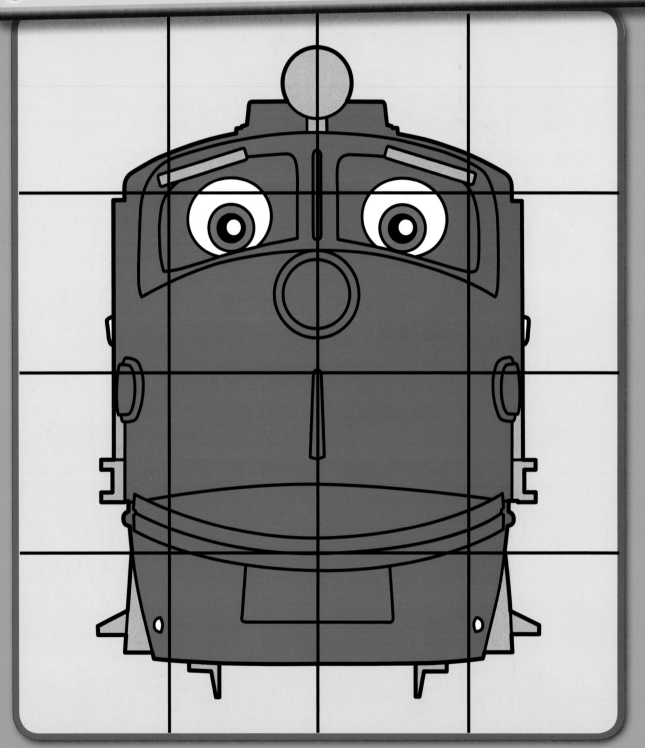

48

"LET'S RIDE THE RAILS"!

HOW MANY RED TRAINS?

How many red trains can you see in the boxes below?

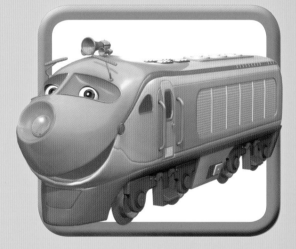

DOT TO DOT

Join the dots to finish this picture of the ice-cream chugger, Frostini. Then colour it in.

ODD ONES OUT

Frostini's ice-cream is made of only the best ingredients, but can you find the odd ones out? Why don't they belong?

Strawberry

 =

Chocolate

 =

Banana

 =

What's your favourite flavour?

WILSON'S MAZE

Wilson has got lost on his way back from the safari park! Lead him through the maze to the Chuggington depot.

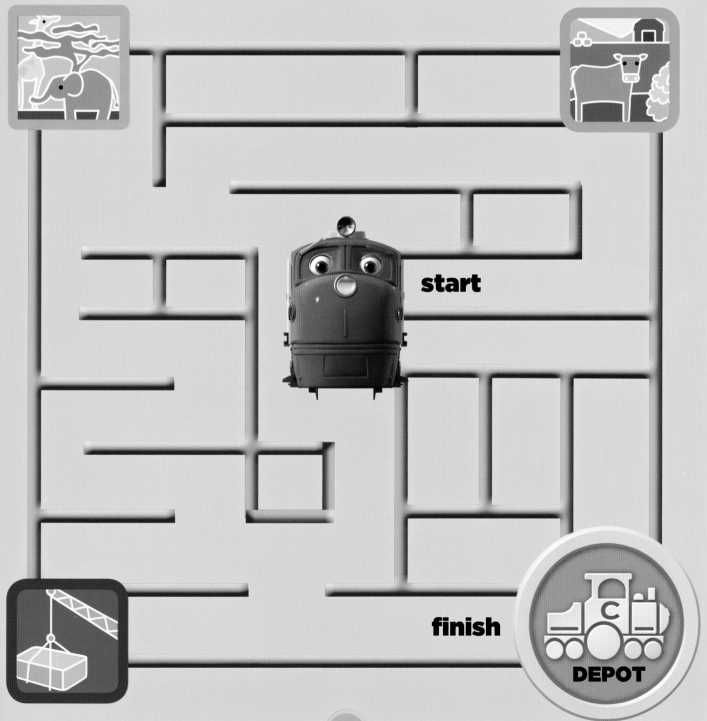

start

finish

DEPOT

CAN'T CATCH KOKO

1 One morning, Chuggington's fastest train, Harrison, was in the repair shed being fixed. **"I need to get fixed fast, Morgan, or I won't be able to make the delivery run tonight,"** Harrison said.

2 Koko zoomed into the fuel yard to tell Wilson and Brewster about Harrison. Someone really fast would have to do the night run for him...she could do it!

3 Koko begged Dunbar to let her go on the night run. **"I bet I can do the fastest run ever,"** she begged. Dunbar thought it would be a good experience for her, but Wilson and Brewster would have to go with her too.

4 The three chuggers loaded up and got ready to ride the rails! **"Now remember Chuggers, stay together,"** Vee warned.

5 As soon as the tunnel light appeared, Koko shot off ahead of Wilson and Brewster. **"Bet you can't catch Koko!"** she shouted, keen to make a speedy delivery.

"CAN'T CATCH KOKO!"

6 Wilson and Brewster finally caught up with Koko. They came out of the tunnel and gasped at the beautiful, moonlit countryside around them. Koko whizzed ahead again, but Wilson was worried – they had to stay together.

7 Further ahead, Koko hid down a side track and waited for Wilson and Brewster to appear. Koko could hear them getting closer and closer...

CHUGGA CHUGGA CHOO CHOO!

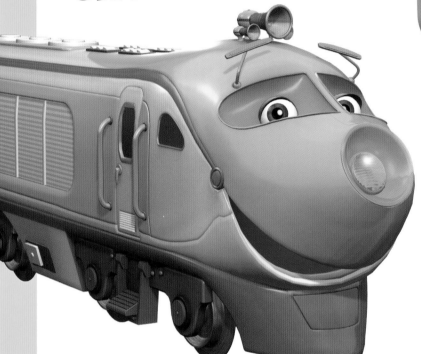

8 "BOOooo!"

Koko yelled as she made the boys jump in surprise.

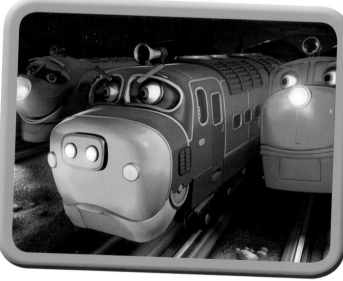

9 Brewster nearly fell off the track - he got cross with Koko.
"If you weren't such a slow coach you would've seen me. Brewster's a slow coach, Brewster's a slow coach!" she teased in a singsong voice.

10 The chuggers didn't have time to waste if they wanted to make the delivery on time. But then...

CREAK, CLUNK, SPLUTTER!

11 Koko's engine started making a funny noise and she stopped moving! She cried for help but Wilson and Brewster were too far ahead to hear her.

12 Wilson and Brewster realised Koko was nowhere in sight. There were no lights on anywhere – there must have been a power cut. **"Phew, good job we're not electric,"** said Brewster. They both gasped – but Koko was!

13 Meanwhile, Koko was feeling sad and lonely. Just then she heard something in the distance.

"WHO'S THERE?"

14 Wilson and Brewster had come back! With no power in the tracks to charge her engine, now Koko was the slow coach.
"I'm sorry I teased you, Brewster," she said, quietly.

15 At the depot, Dunbar and Morgan were worried about the trainees alone in the dark. Suddenly, Wilson came along, towing Koko behind him.

WOOOOoo!"
"WOOOOoo!"

16 cried Wilson, making a loud siren noise. **"Breakdown chugger coming through!"** Then Koko told Dunbar that Brewster was doing the night run all on his own.

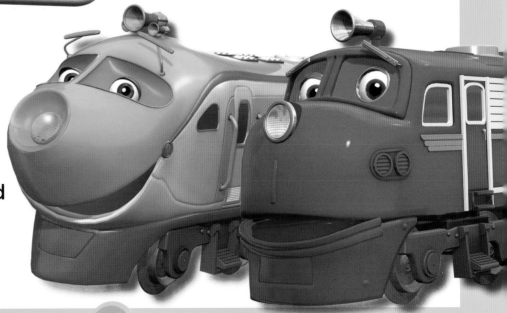

17 At last, the power was back and Koko whizzed up and down the track excitedly. Vee made an announcement. **"You'll be pleased to know that Brewster's delivered everything on schedule."**

18 Wilson and Koko were so proud of their friend. And Koko promised to never, ever call Brewster a slow coach again!

ODD ONES OUT

Felix the farmer grows lots of fruit and vegetables. Which of these are the odd ones out? Why don't they belong in the group?

ACTION CHUGGER

Action Chugger is a super-hero! His jet engines help him fly from one adventure to the next. The trainees hope to grow up to be just like him.

"I'm helpful, I'm strong, I get the job done!"

MTAMBO

Mtambo takes people around the safari park so they can see all the animals. He's travelled all over the world and the trainees love to hear about his adventures.

It's time for Safari!

GUESS WHO?
This picture has got all mixed up.
Can you tell which chugger it is?

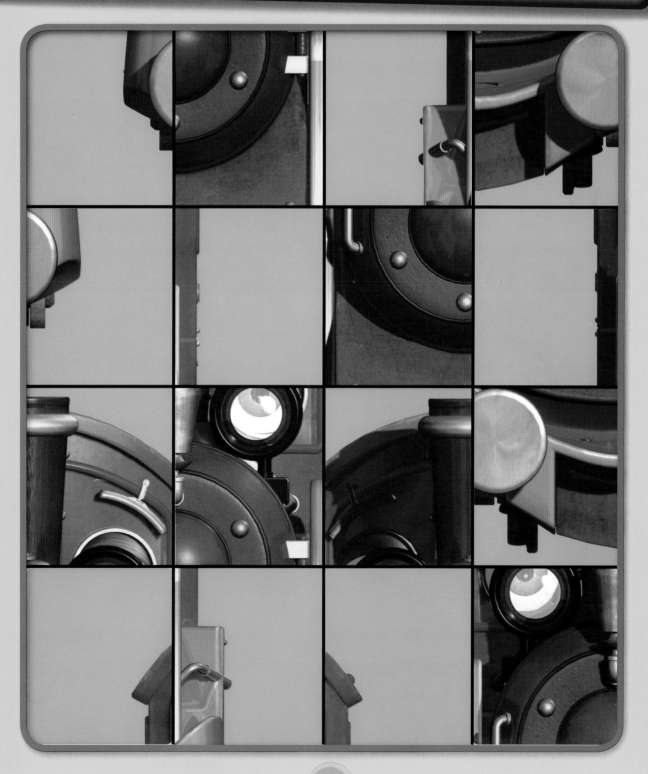

WHAT'S THE SOUND?

These chuggers all make sounds, but can you match the noise to the chugger?

1 "BEEP, BEEP!"

a

2 "PUFF, PUFF, PUFF!"

b

3 "CHUGGA, CHOO, CHOO!"

c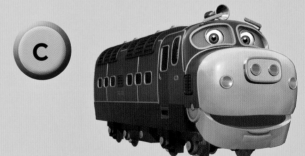

4 "HONK, HONK!"

d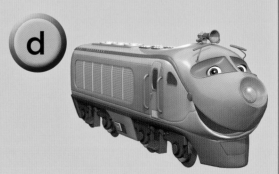

64

COLOURING FUN
Have fun colouring in this speedy young chugger.

TRAINTASTIC!

COPY AND COLOUR

Copy this picture of Action Chugger into the grid on the next page, using the lines as a guide. Then colour your drawing.

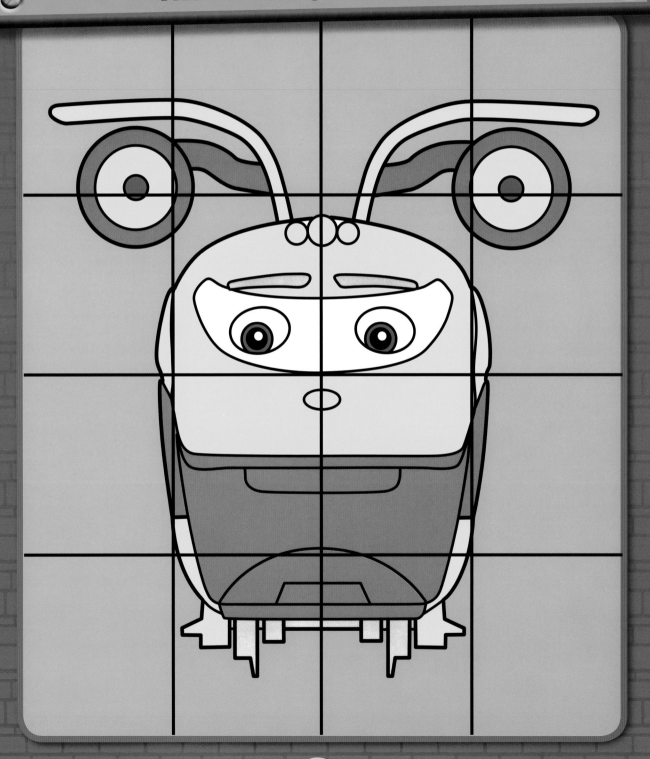

"I'M HELPFUL, I'M STRONG!"

SHAPE FINDER

Look at the pictures carefully. Can you find these shapes? Can you point to them.

 **Triangle**

Square

 **Circle**

Rectangle

What shape do you see?
Count the corners
– one, two, three!

_____

This shape has two long
sides and two short sides.

_____

This shape starts at the top and goes all the way round. What can it be?

This shape has four sides all the same length.

_____

SPOT THE DIFFERENCE
Can you find six differences between the two pictures below? Circle the ones you find.

HONKING HORNS!

Well done for finding all the differences!

CALLEY

Calley is Dunbar's assistant. She loves flashing her yellow warning lights when she's out on an emergency.

"Absotootly!"

KOKO'S MAZE

Koko needs to take Peckham back to Morgan's repair shed. Can you help her find the way?

start

finish

WAKE UP WILSON

1 One evening, Wilson and Koko were chasing each other around the park. **"Can't catch me!"** shouted Wilson, laughing. **"Here I come, slow coach,"** Koko replied, zooming after him.

ZOOOOOM!

2 Vee announced it was bedtime for the chuggers. **"You need an early night, Wilson. You have your first mail run tomorrow."** Wilson wanted to have fun with Koko – he had forgotten all about the mail run!

3 At the roundhouses, Koko and Wilson dared each other to stay awake. They lasted as long as they could, then Wilson heard Koko snoring. **"Wahay, I won,"** whispered Wilson, before falling asleep too.

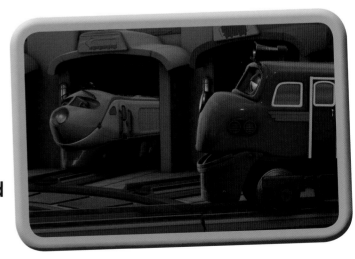

4 In the morning, Wilson chugged sleepily towards the rolling stock yard and coupled up to a mail car. **"You've practiced with this mail car lots of times before,"** said Dunbar, and reminded him what to do.

YAWN

5 By the time Wilson reached the second station stop, he felt really sleepy.

ZZZZZ

6 Oil Can Eddie spotted Wilson from the track above. **"Watch out, Wilson, your door's open mate."** Yawning, Wilson thanked Eddie and drove into the tunnel.

7 Wilson felt even sleepier inside the tunnel. It was dark and cosy, just like his roundhouse. He pulled over to the side of the track and fell asleep.

8 Meanwhile, Vee was looking for Wilson. He was supposed to be at the sorting office by noon.

9 Wilson woke up slowly and rolled out of the tunnel. **"I'm here, Vee. Don't worry – I'll catch up,"** he promised, racing off.

10 Back at the depot, Koko overheard Dunbar and Vee talking about Wilson. They were worried he wouldn't make it to the sorting office on time. **"Oh, no! Wilson's tired 'cause I kept him up so late," thought Koko.**

11 She raced off to see if she could help her sleepy friend.

"CHOO CHOO!"

12 Koko soon found Wilson who was asleep again at the side of the track. **"Wake up, Wilson," cried Koko, sounding her horn.** Wilson woke up and gasped. **"Oh no! I've gotta shift my gears!"**

13 At last, Wilson reached the sorting office with the Chuggington post. But the rest of the mail had already been taken to the branch stations.

14 **"The Chuggington post has never been late before,"** said the postmistress, sadly. Wilson felt terrible. It was all his fault.

15 Suddenly, he had an idea... he could sort the mail now and take it to all the branch stations himself. It would take a long time but the postmistress agreed to give it a try.

16 The mail was sorted into sacks, before being loaded into Wilson's car. Then Wilson dropped off a sack at each station.

17 At last, Wilson chugged into the depot. He'd done it! He had delivered all the Chuggington mail. **"I'm sorry I let you all down. It won't happen again,"** Wilson promised.

18 And it didn't! That night, Wilson had lots of sleep, and the next morning, he did the mail run on time.

COPY AND COLOUR

Use the grid to help you copy this traintastic picture of Koko onto the page. Then colour it in.

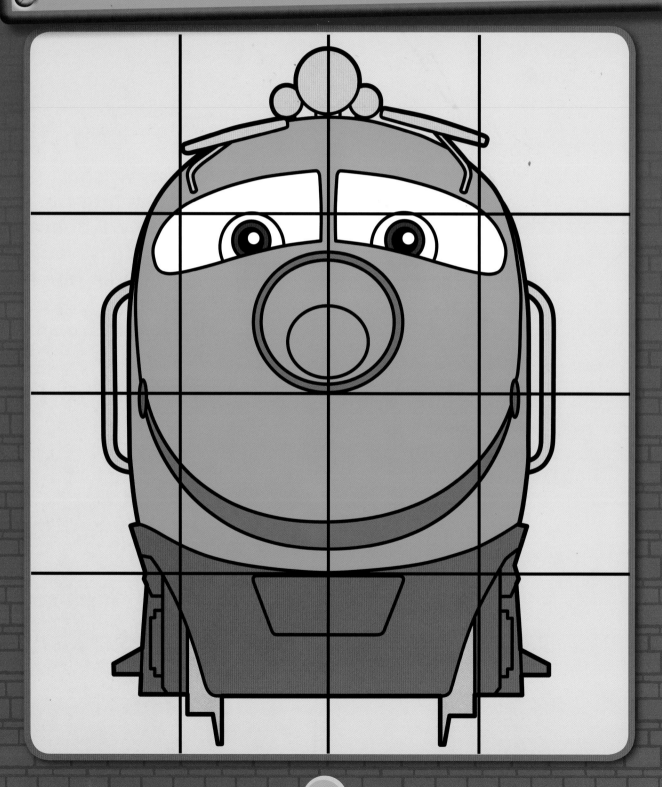

CHUGGA, CHUGGA, CHOO CHOO...

COUNTING FUN
Count the number of things in each group.
Write the number in each box.

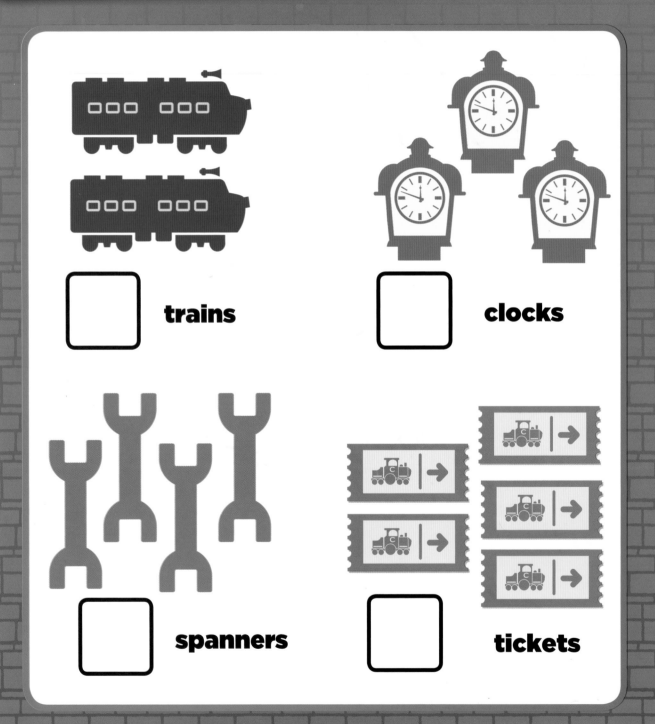

trains

clocks

spanners

tickets

MATCHING PAIRS

How many pairs of matching chuggers can you find? Who doesn't match?

I can find ☐ matching pairs.

_____ and _____ don't match.

WHICH TUNNEL?

Brewster needs to deliver bananas to the safari park. Which tunnel takes him there?

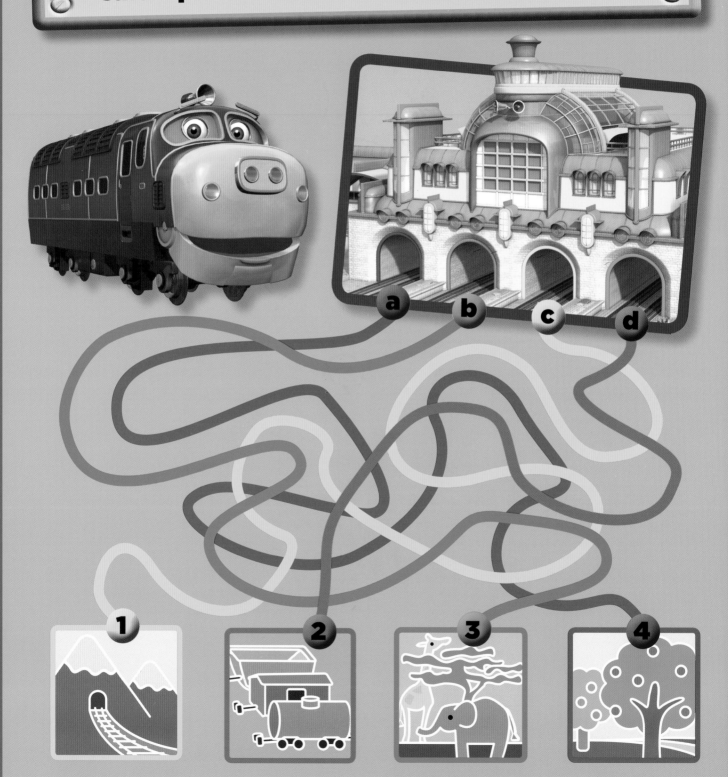

a   b   c   d

1   2   3   4

DOT TO DOT

Join the dots to finish this picture of Dunbar.
Then have fun colouring it in.

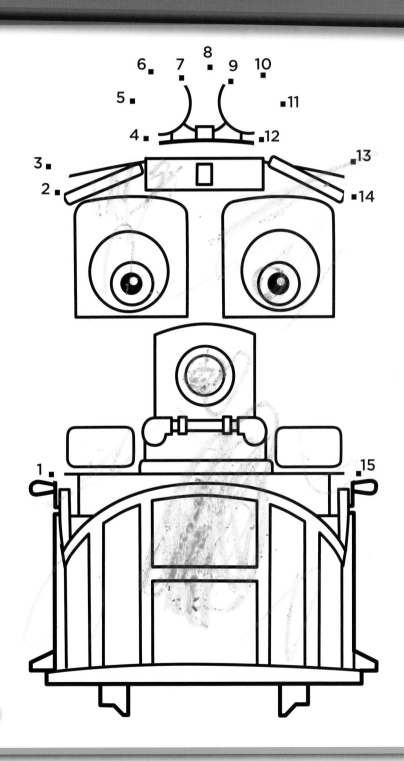

COLOUR THE SCENE

Use your favourite crayons to colour
this Chuggington scene.

WORDSEARCH

Can you find these traintastic words in the grid below?

HORN   CLOCK   BUMPER

FUNNEL   WHEEL

B	U	M	P	E	R
F	D	P	R	Y	A
U	Q	O	J	R	C
N	W	H	E	E	L
N	K	O	I	K	O
E	J	R	D	V	C
L	C	N	R	S	K

IRVING

Irving handles the rubbish and recycling. He uses his two big sweeper brushes to keep Chuggington clean.

Recycle it!

WHAT GOES WHERE?

Match the things below to the different places around Chuggington.

1.

2.

3.

4.

5.

6.

a
Coast

b
Orchard

c
Farm

d
Safari Park

e
Repair Shed

f
Farmers Market

CAN YOU FIND?

Can you spot these items in the scene below?
Circle the ones you find.

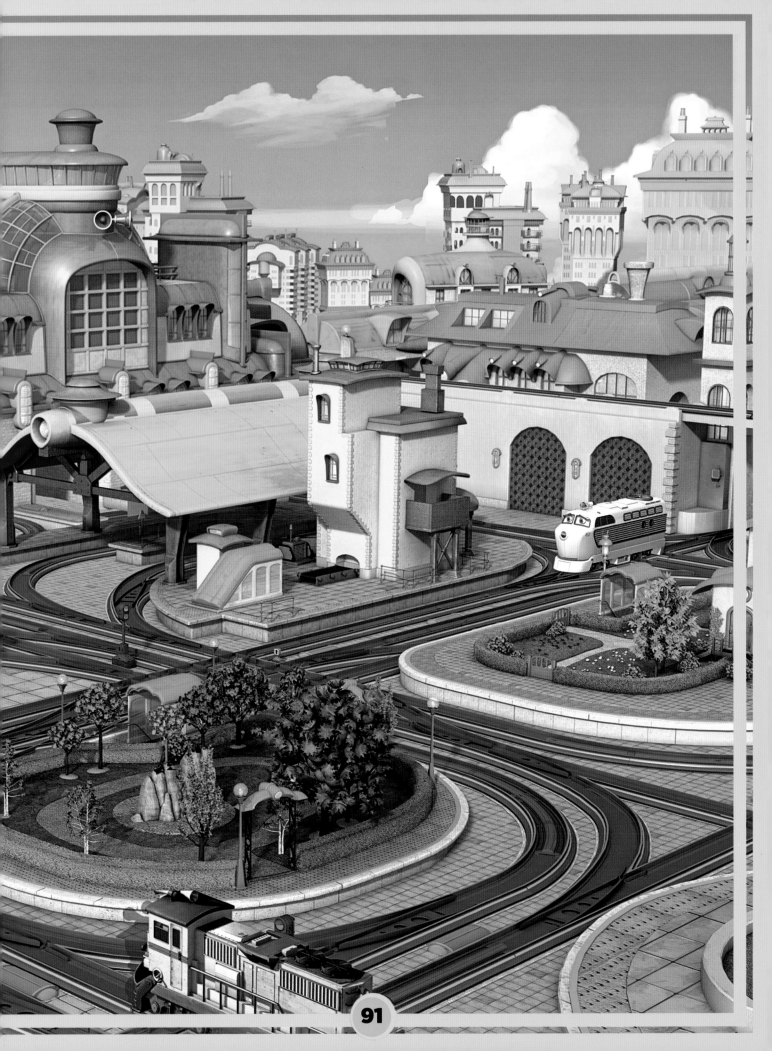

ANSWERS

Page 9

B	T	I	O	M	E
E	M	E	R	Y	A
C	R	D	B	K	J
W	I	L	S	O	N
E	K	W	I	K	K
W	J	A	C	O	Y
D	U	N	B	A	R

Page 10

Trail b) leads to Wilson

Page 20

Page 24

1 and 4 match exactly

Page 26-27

Page 28

Jigsaw piece b) doesn't fit

Page 29

Page 33

There are 4 green trains

Page 40

1. 7 o'clock
2. 11 o'clock
3. 2 o'clock
4. 6 o'clock
5. 9 o'clock
6. 4 o'clock

Page 42

Harrison is the biggest train
Zephie is the smallest train

Page 45

Action Chugger

Page 46

Page 50

There is 1 red train

Page 52

The cabbage, sandwich and toast are the odd ones out

Page 53

Page 60

The ice-cream and chocolate do not belong

Page 63

Old Puffer Pete

Page 64

Page 70-71

Page 73

Page 82

2 trains, 3 clocks,
4 spanners, 5 tickets

Page 83

There are 7 matching pairs
2 and 15 don't match

Page 84

Tunnel b) leads to the Safari Park

Page 87

B	U	M	P	E	R
F	D	P	R	Y	A
U	Q	O	J	R	C
N	W	H	E	E	L
N	K	O	I	K	O
E	J	R	D	V	C
L	C	N	R	S	K

Page 89

1. c
2. a
3. b
4. f
5. e
6. d

Visit  VIRTUAL CHUGGINGTON

www.chuggington.com

Type this code into the website for a special game! CHGMAG1

Now you can ride the rails with Wilson, Koko and Brewster!

Honk your horns! Here in Chuggington we need more little engines to join us and keep things ship-shape. That means you, trainee!

- ○ **Paint your own engine**
- ○ **Meet the chuggers**
- ○ **Finish training tasks**
- ○ **Play games**
- ○ **Earn badges**

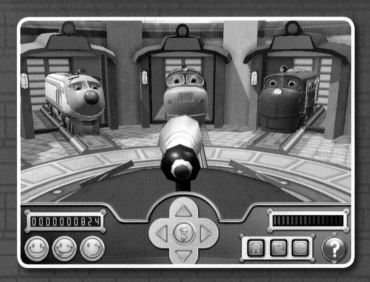

Attention grown-ups!

Virtual Chuggington is a digital world where children can experience life from the same perspective as the engines. Think of it as a digital train set, one with an open-ended play pattern and storytelling capability that will awaken your child's sense of wonder!

Join us here, won't you? We can't wait to learn, work and play together!

www.chuggington.com